To Struan

Happy reading!

Mike Nicholson

This book belongs to

_____

_____

For Finn, who definitely deserves a wee tartan ted ~ J.L.

For Carole and Derek ~ thanks for your amazing Nethybridge hospitality ~ M.N

Picture Kelpies is an imprint of Floris Books. First published in 2016 by Floris Books. Text © 2016 Mike Nicholson. Illustrations © 2016 Jo Litchfield
Mike Nicholson and Jo Litchfield assert their right under the Copyright, Designs and Patents Act 1988 to be recognised as the Author and Illustrator of this Work
All rights reserved. No part of this book may be reproduced without prior permission of Floris Books, Edinburgh. www.florisbooks.co.uk
The publisher acknowledges subsidy from Creative Scotland towards the publication of this volume. British Library CIP Data available
ISBN 978-178250-254-8. Printed in Malaysia

Thistle Games
A braw Scots story for bairns

MIKE NICHOLSON
AND JO LITCHFIELD

Picture
Kelpies

Thistle Games is here – the event of the year! –
And everyone's joining together.
Now music and dancing, and great strength and speed,
Will be tested, whatever the weather!

Spectators chat as competitors stretch,
The excitement is reaching its peak.
The wee ones might struggle to see through the crowd,
Squeeze through and we'll all have a *keek!*

The Games start with races for every age,
Each child here is eager to run,
The serious athletes have fancy new kit,
While others are in it for fun.

It was Heather who won the top medals last year,
But she's resting and eating a cookie!
You won't find her sprinting a metre today,
With one of her legs in a *stookie*.

Wee Caitlin steps up for her first Highland dance,
Her tartan is blue, green and white.
She's dreamed of this moment and takes a deep breath,
Determined that she'll get it right.

At the end of her turn Caitlin curtseys with style,
But will she score ten points or fewer?
She has no idea she'll be getting top marks,
As both of the judges look *dour*.

Big Euan's convinced
   he's the strongest man here,
His training should make him the best.

Throwing hammer, then shot put
   and tossing the caber,
Each object provides a new test.

As ever wee Archie
  can't wait to join in,
He loves to make anything hurtle.

He picks up a stick
  from the wooden craft stall,
And launches a wee porridge *spurtle*.

The Ross twins line up and get on their marks –
It's time for the three-legged race.
With ankles bound tightly, it's tough to set off,
And harder to gather some pace.

As zigzagging partners collide on the track,
They fall with their arms and legs swinging.
Mairi drags Hamish through cowpats and mud,
They manage first place but they're *mingin!*

The next sporting feat
is the mighty high jump,
And Jeannie the vet is a pro.

She's limbering up
as it's almost her turn,
The tension is starting to grow.

Jeannie sprints, leaps and soars
   but on the way down,
She wobbles just like Humpty Dumpty:

She topples and tumbles
   and falls to the ground
And feels like a bit of a *numpty*.

The colourful pipe band parades once an hour,
The mace spinning high in the air.
They all march in time as the big drums are thumped,
Folk stop what they're doing to stare.

The Docherty family are watching the fun,
While picnicking out on their rugs,
But Isla can't cope with the noise, it's too much –
She clamps her hands over her *lugs!*

The pipe band have worked up a hunger and thirst,
They queue at the fish and chip van.
It's hot, fast and frantic to cook for this crowd,
The staff want a rest and a fan.

Mr Craig has asked Struan to tidy the bins.
He's offered the wee lad a fiver,
But he finds his son hiding and scoffing some chips,
And yells, "I'm not paying a *skiver!*"

Agnes is tired and her mind has gone blank,
She's been busily baking for days.
With oatcakes and shortbread and tablet on sale,
Her goodies get plenty of praise.

But someone is quietly pinching the treats,
Though the scene appears perfectly calm.
It's Shona the pony who's helping herself
While Agnes just sits in a *dwam*.

The quickest hill runners dash back down the slope,
Over rocky and heathery ground.
There's one lap to go past the crowds in the field,
With clapping and cheers all around.

Miss Dunbar from school has found the run tough,
She's lost all her puff and she's purple.
Her class shout "Come on!" but her legs are so stiff,
The best she can do now is *hirple*.

It's the last strong-man task:
  the fifty-pound weight,
Swung over a bar
  hoisted high.

Young Callum struts over to
  challenge Big Euan:
"Just watch while I make this
  stone fly!"

Callum turns to the crowd
    and gets them to clap,
It's clearly a moment
    he's savouring.

He stoops, strains and shouts –
    but it won't budge an inch!
Young Callum's brave talk
    was just *havering*.

It's late and it's time for the day's last event:
The annual town tug-of-war.
All of the children compete with the grown-ups,
And pull the big rope with a roar.

But Robbie has sneaked in a bag full of midgies,
To free them he just has to tweak it.
The cloud of wee bugs makes the grown-ups go mad –
The kids win, cause Robbie's been *sleekit!*

The crowds start to leave – it's the end of the Games,
They've all had their fun for this year.
With arms full of trophies and wee tartan teds,
Everyone's full of good cheer.

Mr Brodie triumphantly plays each request:
"Abba!" "The Beatles!" "Vivaldi!"
His fingers are flying, his cheeks bursting out –
This piper is *gie-ing it laldy!*

Dour – stern, severe

Dwam – a blank or dreamy state of mind

Gie-ing it laldy – giving it energy and enthusiasm

Havering – talking nonsense

Hirple – to limp, hobble

Keek – a peek, to glance

Lugs – ears

Mingin – stinky

Numpty – a silly person

Skiver – someone who dodges work

Sleekit – sneaky, cunning

Spurtle – a short stick for stirring porridge

Stookie – a plaster cast